BIBLE HERO ADVENTURES

Old Testament

Group
Loveland, Colorado

Bible Hero Adventures: Old Testament

Contributors

Lois Keffer, Mike Nappa, Cindy Nelson, Joani Schultz, Liz Shockey, Jennifer Root Wilger, and Beth Rowland Wolf

Credits

Editor: Lois Keffer
Senior Editor/Creative Products Director: Joani Schultz
Copy Editor: Ann Marie Rozum
Art Director: Helen H. Lannis
Cover Art Director: Liz Howe
Computer Graphic Artist: Ray Tollison
Cover Illustrator: Paula Becker
Illustrator: Paula Becker
Production Manager: Gingar Kunkel

ISBN 1-55945-607-8
10 9 8 7 6 5 4 3 2 1   05 04 03 02 01 00 99 98 97 96

Printed in Hong Kong.

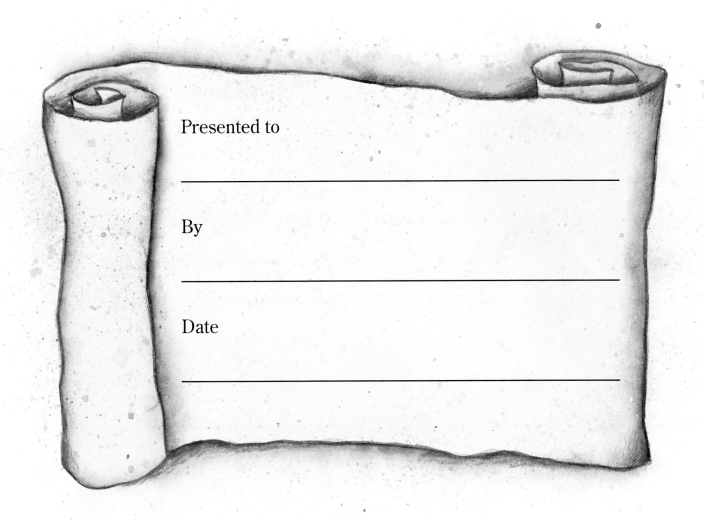

Presented to

_____

By

_____

Date

_____

Contents

Introduction

This book holds the promise of hours of fascinating reading and Bible-learning fun for you and your preschooler. Through its pages you'll introduce your child to some of the greatest characters of the Bible—people whose lives shaped history.

The unique, involving style of these stories allows children to interact with Bible heroes through motions, rhymes, and questions. You'll be amazed as you watch your child gain an exciting first-hand perspective of how God works in the lives of those who trust him.

As preschoolers grow to love the characters they meet in these pages, they'll learn that Bible heroes come in all shapes, sizes, and styles— from valiant warriors like Samson to sweet little grandmothers like Naomi. After all, Bible heroes are just ordinary people who love and trust our extraordinary God!

Use these engaging stories to fill your child's mind with good things from God's Word. It's never too soon to challenge your child to be a faith hero who trusts God in every situation.

Sarah's Surprise

(From Genesis 18:1-15; 21:1-3)

I was sitting inside my tent one day
When three strangers passed our way.
(Walk three fingers across palm.)

My husband, Abraham, bowed down low
For these were important men, you know.
(Bow.)

He said, "Please rest and wash your feet
While my wife and I get you something to eat."

So they sat down beneath a tree
And Abraham came to talk to me.

"Please make some bread. Be quick! Let's hurry."
(Cup hands around mouth and whisper loudly.)
So I jumped up and worked in a flurry.

Flour, salt, and a little yeast,
Now help me stir—we'll make a feast!
(Pretend to stir.)

Abraham cooked a tender roast.
Don't you think he's quite a fine host?
(Put hands on hips and nod proudly.)

The guests enjoyed the food we made,
While Abraham stood close by in the shade.

"Where's your wife, Sarah?" one man asked.
When I heard my name, I stopped and gasped.
(Gasp.)

Abraham answered, "In the tent over there."
Then I began to listen with care.
(Cup hand to ear.)

"I'll come back next year," said guest number one.
"And when I come back, she'll have a son."
(Fold arms and nod.)

"A son?" I thought, "But I'm too old!
I'll never have a baby to hold.
(Shake head.)

"My husband and I are wrinkled and gray—
No child for us! No baby! No way!"

A son? Oh, no! Ha ha! Hee hee!
I felt the laughter rising up in me.
(Hold stomach and laugh.)

A son? At my age? It must be a joke!
I laughed so hard I started to choke.

Laughter made tears roll down my cheek
(run finger down cheek),
But then our guest began to speak.

"Why does she laugh about having a son?
By this time next year, it will be done!"

(Shake finger.)

"I didn't laugh, sir." I was scared, so I lied.
"Oh, yes you did," our guest replied.
(Nod head.)

Finally our guests went on their way;
But I tell you, I'll never forget that day.
(Shake head.)

Can you tell what happened? I'll give you a clue.
What our visitor said really came true!

Before the year was past and done,
I gave birth to a beautiful son!
(Pretend to hold a baby.)

You've never seen such a fine little boy.
He was Abraham's pride and joy.
(Fold arms and nod.)

We named him Isaac—that means "laughter"—
Because we lived happily ever after.
(Cross hands over heart.)

Now, listen to me because I am wise.
You've learned how God gave me a huge surprise.

And someday God may surprise you, too.
(Point at child.)
For there isn't anything God can't do.

Faithful Caleb

(From Numbers 13:1–14:25)

The Lord told Moses, "Go explore!
(Point forward.)
See what your new land has in store."

So Moses gathered every clan
And told them what the Lord had planned.

"Attention all tribes, small and grand!
(Cup hands together, then open arms wide.)
Let's go spy on Canaan land!
(Shield eyes and look around.)

"Reuben, Ephraim, Benjamin,
Send us some of your very best men.
(Make a beckoning motion.)

"Manasseh, Asher, Gad, and Dan,
Who will you send? Who'll be your man?

"Naphtali and Simeon,
Issachar and Zebulun—

"We need a leader from each tribe.
(Count on fingers.)
We'll wait until they've all arrived.

"Eleven of twelve tribes are here.
Let's call to Judah loud and clear.
(Cup hands around mouth and shout next line.)

"Judah, Judah, send a spy!"
"We'll send Caleb—he's our guy."
(Put hands on hips.)

Twelve strong men went to explore
(march)
Each mountain, valley, lake, and shore.

They went to spy on the people there
(shield eyes and look around)
To see just how they lived, and where.

Did they live in cities tall
(look up)
With heavy gates and giant walls?
(Spread arms wide.)

Were they weak or were they strong?
(Hold up arm and make a muscle.)
A tiny tribe or mighty throng?

They looked at all the plants to see
(shield eyes and look around)
What kind of fruit grew on the trees.
(Reach up and pluck imaginary fruit.)

Pomegranates, grapes, and figs
(point in three different directions)—
Everything was really big!
(Spread arms wide.)

They found a bunch of grapes so thick
They had to hang it from a stick.
(Pretend to hold up a stick with something heavy attached.)

They cut the branches from the vine.
(Pretend to clip an imaginary vine.)
That bunch of grapes looked mighty fine!
(Rub tummy.)

For 40 days they spied on that place
(pretend to look through spy glasses),
And then they left without a trace.
(Turn around and tiptoe several steps.)

Twelve spies returned with fruit in hand.
(Hold hands out as if full of fruit.)
Brave Caleb said, "Let's take this land."

But others said, "We can't attack.
Those guys are strong—they'll
fight right back!"
(Put up fists.)

"We're grasshoppers compared to them
(*hold fingers as if measuring an inch*)—
There's just no way that we can win!
(*Shake head.*)

"Besides, their land is not so great.
(*Cross arms stubbornly.*)
We might find better if we wait.

"Let's pick up camp and travel far
(*point far away*)
Before they find out who we are."

While families packed up all around,
Caleb and Joshua stood their ground.
(*Stand with hands on hips, feet planted slightly apart.*)

"We saw giants strong and tall
(*hold up arms and make a muscle*),
But the Lord our God will make them fall.
(*Make a downward motion with hand.*)

"With God's help we'll take their land!

(*Point
upward.*)
God will
help his
people stand."
(*Stand up straight
and tall.*)

The people shook and began to cry
(*quiver with fear*),
"Did you bring us here to die?

"Moses, Aaron! Take us back!
Let's go to Egypt. We're all packed."
(*Make a beckoning motion.*)

Then God spoke from above the tent
(*touch hands over head to form a tent shape*),
"How long until these folks repent?

"How long until they
trust in me?
I'm right here with
them—can't they see?

"I'll send disease, then by and by
These people will get sick and die."

Then Moses prayed, "Lord, please forgive
(fold hands as if praying)
Your chosen people. Let them live.

"Remember your great love today
(put hands over heart);
You've traveled with us all the way."

The Lord said, "Yes, I will forgive.
(Nod head.)
But as surely as I live,

"They'll wander here on desert sand
(spread hands in front of you)—
Not one of them will see that land.
(Cover eyes.)

"They never trust! They only sin.
(Shake head.)
So only Caleb will go in.

"Caleb follows my commands.
His family will have the land."

So when you're tempted to do wrong,
Remember Caleb and be strong.
(Tap side of head.)

Trust the Lord in all you do
(point up to heaven),
And God will take good care of you!

Rahab and the Spies

(From Joshua 2:1-21; 6:1-25)

Have you heard the tale of Rahab
Whose heart was brave and true?
Now listen to her story
And I'll whisper it to you!
(Hold your finger to your lips.)

It started with two Israelite spies
Who came to see the town
(shield eyes with hand),
To decide how to attack it
And make the walls fall down.

The two spies stayed at Rahab's house,
For she had room to spare.
And though they might be enemies,
She made them welcome there.
(Make beckoning gesture.)

But all too soon the king got word
(bring hand to ear)
Of spies inside the gate.
(Point finger and speak with authority.)
He said, "Have Rahab bring those men
Before it is too late."

The spies thought they were done for
(look scared),
But Rahab's plan was wise.
"Come up onto my roof," she said.
(Point up.)
"I'll hide you Israelite spies."

So all three tiptoed to the roof
("tiptoe" fingers across hand)
As quietly as mice.

14

Then Rahab covered them with flax
And said, "That looks quite nice!

"Should soldiers come to look for you,
They won't see anyone there.
(Smile and shake head.)
They'll only see my piles of flax
Drying in the air!"

Then Rahab sent a message
(pretend to write)
And said, "O king, don't worry.
The two men left today at dusk.
You'll catch them if you
hurry."

When the king's men went
away,
The spies said a great big "Whew!"
(Wipe your brow.)
"You've surely saved our lives
today.
Now, what can we do for you?"

Rahab said, "Here's what I ask.
My people are trembling with fear.
(Tremble and look scared.)
I know you serve the living God,
And your army is quite near.

"When you march upon our town
I'll gather my family here.
(Stretch arms out around imaginary family.)
Please say you will not hurt or harm
Anyone I hold dear."

"We will do just as you say,"
The Israelites gave their word.
"Hang this in your window," they
said,
And gave her a scarlet cord.
(Hold hands out, palms up.)

When the day of battle came,
God's army marched round and
round.
(Pretend to march.)

15

Then with a shout and a trumpet blast,
Jericho's walls fell down.
(Raise hands high, then drop them.)

God's people won a great victory!
No one could stand in their way.
(Raise arms in victory.)
But Rahab's family was safe in her house.
No one harmed them that day
(Hug yourself.)

Because brave Rahab had helped the spies,
Though she was just a stranger.
She was willing to keep them safe
And put her own life in danger.

So that's the story of Rahab.
I think she was brave—don't you?
And when you put your trust in God
(point up, then to children),
You can do brave things too!

Deborah's Victory

(From Judges 4–5)

A long time ago, in a place far away,
God's chosen people refused to obey.
(Shake head.)
Although God sent judges to keep them in line
(shake finger),
The Israelites thought they could manage just fine.

A woman named Deborah served Israel as judge.
She helped out when there was a fight or a grudge.
The people would come when they couldn't agree,
And she settled their arguments under a tree.

Sometimes the enemy came TRAMP-A-TRAMP
(stomp feet)—
Stole all their things and took over their camp.
(Pretend to put things in a bag.)
Somehow God's people could not understand
(scratch head and look puzzled)
That they needed God's help to hang on to the land.
(Point toward heaven.)

King Jabin came over to fight them one day
(put up fists),
Just as God's people had gone their own way.

The Lord God decided to let Jabin win
So the people would turn back to God once again.

The people cried out to the Lord, "Help us, please!"
(Clasp hands as if begging for help.)
As Jabin defeated their armies with ease.
With chariots of iron, Jabin couldn't be crueler
(make a mean face);
For 20 years he was a mean, wicked ruler.
(Flash 10 fingers twice.)

The Lord said to Deborah, "Go, gather your men.
Have Barak recruit me 10,000, and then
March up to Mount Tabor and wait patiently.
(March in place, then stop.)
The Lord will deliver his people—you'll see."

The enemy general, Sisera, was ready,
But Deborah's armies were faithful and steady.
When Deborah followed the word of the Lord,
Sisera's huge armies went down by the sword.
(Pretend to fight with swords.)

When the Lord God defeated the enemy that day,
God's people were sure they had conquered.
Hooray!
(Wave arms and cheer.)
But then after all of Sisera's men died,
Sisera himself decided to hide.
(Run in place, then crouch down as if hiding.)

Sisera ran to the tent of Jael
(run in place),
Crept in through the door, then relaxed—all
was well.
(Wipe brow and give a sigh of relief.)
Jael and her family were friends of King Jabin.
Sisera thought surely these people would save him.

Sisera stationed Jael at the door,
Asked for a drink, then lay down on the floor.
(Lie down.)
"If anyone comes up and asks if I'm near,
Just smile sweetly and say, 'He's not here.'"

Well, Sisera was tired from fighting all day.

So, of course he fell sound asleep right away.
But while he lay sleeping there on the floor
(pretend to snore),
Jael killed Sisera—he'd fight no more.

When the king heard that Sisera was defeated
(cup hand to ear),
He pulled his men back—his armies retreated.
(Take three steps backward.)
With God's help the Israelites grew faithful
and strong,
And Deborah and Barak sang a victory song:

"Praise to the Lord, the God of creation!
He helps his people defeat mighty
nations.
The Lord God of Israel has raised volunteers
To march into battle with swords and with spears.

"Wake! Wake up, Deborah! Sing loud and clear.
Sing out a song for all Israel to hear.
Lord, you're our God—you're the only one.
Let all those who love you be strong like the sun!"

Gideon's Teeny-Tiny-Itty-Bitty-Teensy-Weensy Army

(From Judges 6–8)

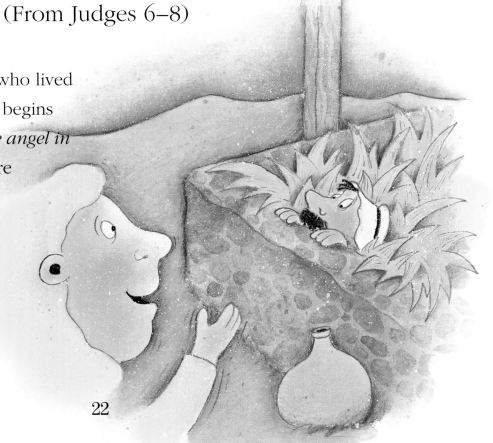

This is a story about Gideon, a man who lived in the land of Israel a long time ago. It begins with a visit from an angel. *(Point to the angel in the picture.)* Here's the angel, but where is Gideon? Hmm...he must be somewhere. Let's look for him.

(Say a child's name), go see if Gideon is under a chair. Not there? Hmm. Gideon might be behind the door. *(Say another child's name)*,

22

go check there. Not there either?

He must be somewhere. Aha! I think I see the top of his head in this picture. Point to it if you see it too. That's right! Gideon is hiding! He's hiding with his wheat to keep it from the Midianites *(MID-ee-uh-nites)*, the enemies of God's people. Can you say Midianites?

Every year the Midianites attacked Israel and stole all of the food and wheat and cattle and sheep and donkeys. They didn't leave anything for Gideon or anyone else to eat. No wonder Gideon was hiding!

Let's pretend we're hiding with Gideon. *(Speak in a hushed voice.)* Huddle close and cover your pretend wheat so no one can steal it!

Suddenly Gideon heard an angel's voice: "The Lord is with you, mighty warrior! Go and save Israel from the Midianites."

Gideon was afraid to fight the Midianites! But the angel promised that God would help Gideon win. So Gideon called all the fighting men in Israel to join him.

When Gideon had gathered all the fighting men, he counted them. Gideon had lots of men, but there were lots and lots and LOTS more Midianites. Each of Gideon's soldiers would have to beat four Midianite soldiers before Gideon could win. *(Hold up one finger on one hand and four fingers on the other hand.)* Do you think you could fight four soldiers all by yourself and still win?

Then God spoke to Gideon and said, "You have too many men. Tell them that anyone who is afraid can go back home."

Yikes! More than half of Gideon's army went home! That meant each of Gideon's soldiers would have to beat more than <u>10</u> Midianite soldiers before Gideon could win! *(Hold up all 10 fingers.)* Do you think you could fight 10 soldiers all by yourself and still win? Oh well, let's wave goodbye to the men who left.

Oh, my! God said there were <u>still</u> too many people in Gideon's army. So Gideon sent practically <u>everybody</u> home. That left him with only a teeny-tiny-itty-bitty-teensy-weensy army to fight against the BIG-HUGE-GIGANTIC-ENORMOUS Midianite army.

It looked like Gideon was going to lose. He didn't have enough fighters! But even though he had only a teeny-tiny-itty-bitty-teensy-weensy army, Gideon still trusted God to help him win.

What do you think Gideon gave his men to fight with? Not swords. *(Pretend to wave a sword.)* Not bows and arrows. *(Pretend to shoot an arrow.)* Gideon gave each of his fight-

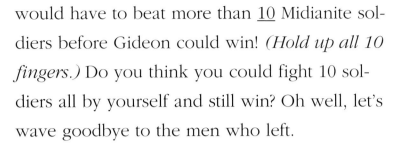

ing men a trumpet and a jar with a burning torch inside. Do you think they could fight with trumpets, jars, and torches? How strange!

In the middle of the night, Gideon's army surrounded the Midianites. When Gideon gave a signal, all his soldiers smashed their jars, held up their torches, and blew their trumpets.

Let's pretend to blow trumpets and hold up torches. *(Trumpet through one cupped hand as you raise the other hand.)*

Then Gideon's soldiers shouted,
"For the Lord and for Gideon!"
Let's shout it with them. "For
the Lord and for
Gideon!"
Do you
know what
happened?

God made all the soldiers in the BIG-HUGE-GIGANTIC-ENORMOUS Midianite army afraid of Gideon. When they heard the trumpets and saw the bright torches, they started fighting among each other and ran away. Gideon won! *(Clap.)*

Well, this story began with a visit from an angel, but let's end it with a song. It goes like this *(sing to the tune of "Twinkle, Twinkle, Little Star"):*

Gideon was scared to fight,
But God helped him do what's right.
Gideon's 300 men
Trusted God to help them win.
You can always trust God too.
When you're scared he'll care for you.

Stronger Than a Lion

(From Judges 13–16)

How strong are you? Pretty strong? Could you lift a heavy box? I bet you could!

What makes you strong? Do you eat good food? Do you exercise? Those things are important to keep our bodies healthy and strong. We're special to God, and God wants us to take good care of our bodies.

I'm going to tell you a Bible story about one of the strongest men who ever lived. His name was Samson, and he was a special servant of God. You can help me tell the story. Whenever I say, "God made Samson strong," hold up your arms and show me your muscles. Can you show me your muscles? Good!

God had special plans for Samson even before Samson was born. For a long time Samson's parents felt sad because they thought they'd never have a baby. Then one day an angel appeared and told them they would have a son—a wonderful boy who would grow up to be a hero and help God's people drive away their enemies.

The angel told them never to cut their son's hair. Samson's long hair would show that he was chosen to be a special servant of God. As long as his hair wasn't cut, God would make Samson strong. (*Show muscles.*)

Sure enough, Samson grew up to be fearless and strong. Once, when Samson was a young man, a lion attacked him. Can you roar like a lion? Ooo, that's scary! Do you think Samson was afraid of the lion? The lion was big and strong. But God made Samson strong, too. (*Show muscles.*) Samson killed the lion with his bare hands.

Another time, Philistine soldiers tried to capture Samson. The Philistines were enemies of God's people. But God made Samson strong. (*Show muscles.*) Just like that (*snap your fingers*), Samson broke the ropes that held him. Using the jawbone of a donkey, Samson struck down 1,000 soldiers!

The Philistine leaders were afraid of Samson. They wanted to know what made him so strong. They knew that Samson was friends with a woman named Delilah, so they promised Delilah bags and bags full of money if she could find out the secret of Samson's strength. Delilah agreed to try to find out Samson's secret and tell it to the men who wanted to capture him. Do you think that was a nice thing for Delilah to do? Can you keep a secret?

Samson loved Delilah. He couldn't keep his

secret from her. He told her that if his hair were cut he would be as weak as any man. That night, while Samson was sleeping, Delilah called in a servant to cut off Samson's hair. Can you make scissors with your fingers? Snip, snip, snip. Samson's hair was gone. And his strength was gone too.

When Samson woke up, the Philistine soldiers captured him. They put him in prison. They were mean to Samson and made him blind. Then the Philistines weren't afraid of him anymore. They laughed at Samson and at God.

But Samson's hair began to grow long again, and God didn't forget about Samson. God still had a plan for him.

The Philistines wanted to celebrate their victory over Samson, so they brought him to a great banquet in the temple of their god Dagon. They wanted to make fun of Samson and of God. Samson prayed to God to make him strong just one more time. *(Show muscles.)*

Samson couldn't see the people, but he could feel the big pillars that held up the temple. Samson pushed against the pillars. Close your eyes. Can you pretend to push like Samson? He pushed harder and harder until the pillars cracked and the roof and walls fell down with a huge CRASH! *(Clap one loud clap.)* God had heard Samson's prayer. God made Samson strong *(show muscles)* once more. Then the Philistines learned that our God is the true God and that the god they worshiped was just a fake.

We can pray to God just as Samson did. Let's pray right now. Thank you, God, for hearing our prayers. Help us remember to pray when we need your help. Amen.

Grandma Naomi

(From Ruth 1–4)

Naomi was a sweet old lady who lived in the country of Moab. She was old enough to be a grandmother. Do you have a grandmother?

Naomi lived with her daughters-in-law, Ruth and Orpah. Naomi thought, "Since my sons have died, I'll never have any grandchildren." That made Naomi very sad. Ruth and Orpah patted Naomi on the shoulder because they loved her and didn't want her to be sad.

Let's pat each other on the shoulder and say, "I'm sorry you're sad."

One day Naomi said to Ruth and Orpah, "I'm going back to Bethlehem, my hometown. But you stay here where you've always lived." Orpah hugged Naomi then waved goodbye.

Let's wave goodbye to Orpah.

But Ruth said to Naomi, "I'll stay with you wherever you go. I will live with your people and worship your God."

So Ruth and Naomi set off on the long walk to Bethlehem. Let's take a long walk around the room. Look—I see Bethlehem off in the distance. Let's keep walking. It's getting closer—let's walk around the room one more time.

Whew! That was a long trip! I'm glad we're finally in Bethlehem. Let's sit down and hear what happened next.

Naomi was glad to see all her old friends in Bethlehem. It was harvest time, so everyone was busy and happy.

Ruth said, "I'll go gather the leftover grain the workers leave in the fields." That night Ruth came home with plenty to eat. "A man named Boaz was very kind to me," Ruth explained to Naomi. "He let me pick up grain in his fields and eat and drink with his workers."

Naomi clapped her hands with joy. Let's clap with her. Yea! Naomi said, "Boaz is our relative. He will take care of us!"

One day Naomi told Ruth to put on her best clothes and visit Boaz. Boaz was sleeping beside his piles of grain. When he woke up, he was surprised to see Ruth waiting quietly at his feet.

Boaz knew that Ruth worked hard and was kind. So he decided to marry her. Let's sing the wedding march together. It goes like this: Dum-dum-de-dum, dum-dum-de dum.

Ruth was a beautiful bride. And guess what—
soon Ruth and Boaz had a baby boy. Naomi got
to be a grandmother after all! Let's rock Naomi's
baby grandson and sing him a little lullaby so he
can go to sleep. What quiet song would you like
to sing?

Ssh! The baby is sleeping. Thank you for being
kind and helping put the baby to sleep. Now
you can rest too.

Hannah, Hannah

(From 1 Samuel 1:1–2:21)

Long ago there lived a woman named Hannah. She was lovely and kind, and her husband loved her very much. But Hannah was sad because she never had any children.

Each year Hannah and her husband made a special trip to the temple to worship God. Hannah stood in front of the temple and prayed to God to give her a son. Hannah felt so sad that she cried as she prayed. Can you show me your saddest face? Oh, my—you look very sad, just like Hannah.

A kind old priest named Eli saw Hannah praying and patted her gently on the shoulder, like this. *(Pat child's shoulder.)* It's nice to show people that we care when they feel sad, and that's just what Eli did. Eli told Hannah that he hoped she would feel better and that God would answer her prayer.

Guess what? God *did* answer Hannah's prayer. The next year she had a fine baby boy. She named the boy Samuel and promised God that when Samuel was old enough, she would take him to the temple where he could serve God all his life.

So when Samuel got a little older, Hannah took him to Eli, the kind old priest. "Here is the boy I prayed for," she told Eli. "I've brought him here to serve God and be your helper, just as I promised." So Samuel grew up in the temple,

and Eli the priest took care of him.

Let's remember Hannah's story with this special rhyme. Listen carefully so you can say what I say and do what I do.

Oh, Hannah, Hannah!
(Shake both hands, palms out.)
What's the matter?
Why are you so sad?
(Frown, rub both eyes.)
Just stop to pray
(fold hands as if praying),
And that's the way
You'll turn your sad to glad!
(Smile, raise hands in praise.)

Well, Hannah, Hannah
(shake both hands, palms out)
Had no baby.
That's why she was sad.
(Frown, rub both eyes.)

She stopped to pray
(fold hands as if praying),
And that's the way
God turned her sad to glad!
(Smile and raise hands in praise.)

Then, Hannah, Hannah
(shake both hands, palms out)
Had a baby!
Samuel was the lad.
(Pretend to rock and cradle a baby.)
She'd stopped to pray
(fold hands as if praying),
And that's the way
God turned her sad to glad!
(Smile and raise hands in praise.)

Now, Hannah, Hannah
(shake both hands, palms out)
Gave God back
Her precious little lad.
(Pretend to cradle a baby in your arms.)

She stopped to pray
(fold hands as if praying)
And that's the way
God turned her sad to glad!
(Smile and raise hands in praise.)

So, Hannah, Hannah
(shake both hands, palms out)
Learned this truth:
Whenever you are sad
(point one finger toward someone),
Just stop to pray
(fold hands as if praying),
And that's the way
God turns your sad to glad!
(Smile and raise hands in praise.)

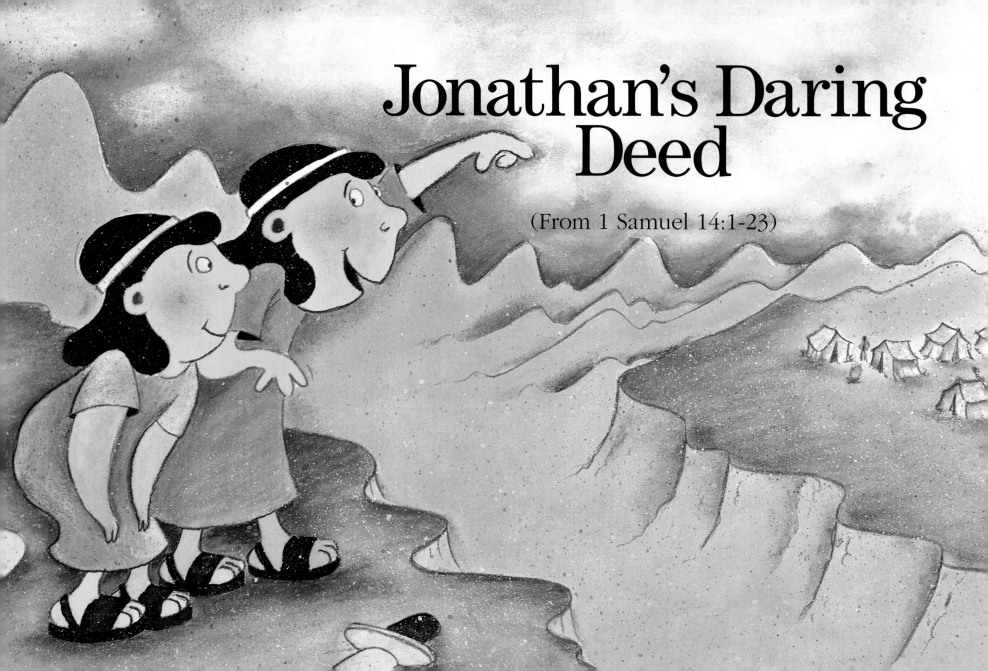

Jonathan's Daring Deed

(From 1 Samuel 14:1-23)

Do you like adventures? Let's go on an adventure right now as I tell you the story of Jonathan and his daring deed. Listen carefully and do what I do.

Jonathan was a prince! *(Pretend to put a crown on your head.)* His father was King Saul, ruler of all God's people in the country of Israel. Israel's neighbors were the Philistines, and they were mean! Show me your meanest face. That's how mean the Philistines were. They would raid towns where God's people lived and steal their animals and crops. The mean Philistines had iron for making swords and spears, but God's people didn't have any swords. Still, God's people were brave and trusted God to help them, so they fought the Philistines anyway.

One day Jonathan said to his friend, "Let's sneak over to the Philistines' camp."

Between the camps of the Israelites and the Philistines were two rocky cliffs. Jonathan and his friend had to climb down one side and climb up the other. Let's pretend to climb up too. *(Pretend to climb up.)* Then they crouched down low so the Philistines wouldn't see them. Quick! Hide, so you won't be spotted! *(Crouch low.)*

Then Jonathan had an idea. He whispered to his friend, *(whisper)* "Let's let the Philistines see us. God will protect us!"

So Jonathan and his friend jumped out from behind the rocks. *(Jump up.)* The

39

Philistine soldiers saw them at once! *(Point.)*

The Philistine soldiers yelled to Jonathan and his friend, "Come up here and we'll teach you a lesson!"

Jonathan said to his friend, "Follow me. We'll fight the Philistines and win. God will help us." There were more than 20 Philistines against Jonathan and his friend! Do you think Jonathan could win?

God helped brave Prince Jonathan. He and his friend won the battle against 20 Philistines. When the rest of the Philistines saw what had happened, they panicked and started to run away.

King Saul and his army peered across the valley. *(Shade eyes with hand.)* They could see that something was wrong in the Philistine camp. King Saul said to his men, "Count the soldiers and see who is missing." So they counted…one, two, three, four… *(Count fingers.)* When they were done counting, they reported to the king, "Your son and his friend are gone!"

Quickly the king called his troops to cross the valley and help Prince Jonathan. When King Saul's soldiers got to the Philistine camp, they found the Philistines fighting each other! Jonathan and his friend were not hurt at all. King Saul was relieved! *(Wipe brow with back of hand.)* He was glad that God had protected his son.

Then King Saul and his army joined the fight. They chased the Philistines to the left. *(Clap hands to the left.)* They chased them to the right. *(Clap hands to the right.)* They chased the Philistines right out of their land! *(Run in place.)*

God helped Prince Jonathan and King Saul win a great victory. Through Jonathan's daring deed, the Lord saved Israel. Praise the Lord! Hooray! *(Raise hands and clap.)*

A Wise Woman

(From 1 Samuel 25:1-35)

Listen, young friends, to this little tale
Of a wise young woman named Abigail.

Everyone said that she was a beauty
(flutter fingers around your face),
But her husband was mean and selfish and snooty.
(Stick your nose in the air.)

They lived in the desert and all was just fine—

"'Til that neighbor moved in," Nabal said with
a whine.
(Make a mean face.)

That neighbor was
David who
soon would
be king.

(Pretend to put on a crown.)
"A man like no other," the women would sing.

David had soldiers—men brave and strong.
(Make a muscle.)
When he moved to the desert, he took them along.
(Make a beckoning motion.)

They were hiding from Saul, who was chasing them all.
(Look behind you.)
King Saul meant to kill them in a terrible brawl.
(Punch the air with your fists.)

When they went to the desert to escape King Saul's fury,
They couldn't take food; they were in such a hurry.
(Pump arms as if running.)

Their stomachs were empty and starting to growl.
(Rub your tummy.)
They needed some food so they went on the prowl.
(Tiptoe with fingertips.)

They found herds of sheep belonging to Nabal
And imagined them all on a dining room table.
(Lick your lips.)

So they asked Nabal how much he could share.
To men who were hungry, it seemed only fair.

But Nabal was foolish and selfish and greedy.
He said, "Get out now! Go on—make it speedy!
(Point away.)

"There's only enough food for me and my own.
I have nothing for you, not even a bone."
(Shake your finger.)

Said David, "Let every man sharpen his sword.
(Pretend to wave a sword.)
We'll show this bad man that it's not right to hoard."

David's 400 men stood ready to fight
(put hands on hips),
All because Nabal wouldn't give them a bite.

"Trouble is coming," the servants all said.
(Shake with fear.)
"All because Nabal won't share any bread."

"Abigail," they cried, "You must save the day!
(Clasp hands as if begging.)
Your husband has sent David's army away.

David's soldiers were kind—they kept us from harm.
But they found only selfishness here on our farm."

Abigail said, "Gather food!
Hurry, hurry!
(Pretend to gather food.)
"We'll give it to David—then
we won't have to worry.

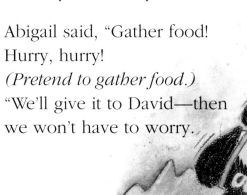

Nope.

"Now bring me those donkeys and load them
with care.
(Pretend to load donkeys.)
We must leave quite soon, or we won't have
a prayer.

"Fetch 200 loaves of the best bread to eat.
Get lamb chops and grain, and figs plump
and sweet.
(Rub your tummy.)

"Go quickly, good servants! Don't let Nabal find you.
Give David this food—I'll be right behind
you.

"Don't let Nabal know—he's
selfish and bad.
If he knows of my plan, he'll be
frightfully mad."
(Make an angry face.)

Abigail bowed low before David's feet
And said, "Take this food that I've brought
you to eat.
(Hold hands out to offer food.)

"My husband was wrong when he sent you away.
We owe you a favor and I'm here to pay."

Then Abigail gave him a beautiful smile
(draw a smile on your face)
And said, "You'll be a great king in a while.
(Pretend to put a crown on your head.)

"I know God will bless you in all that you do.
So please take these gifts that I offer to you.
(Offer gifts.)

"Then when you're king, you'll have peace of mind,
Remembering that you were careful and kind."

David said, "Hmm. What she says is quite wise."
Then he offered his hand and helped her to rise.
(Extend your hand.)

He said, "Praise the Lord! Your wisdom is great.
(Point to your head.)
You've saved me from hurting a man that I hate.

"I'm glad that you stopped me from being too hasty.
And thanks for the food—it looks good and tasty!
(Rub your tummy.)

"Let's enjoy this great feast—all fighting will cease.
I've heard your good words, now please go
in peace."

So Abigail left with joy in her heart.
(Draw a heart on your chest.)
In God's plan for peace, she'd had a big part.

Abigail was wise and so very polite.
(Fold hands and bow.)
To our loving God, she was quite a delight!

God can help you be a wise person, too.
Just be loving and kind in all that you do.

Good News and
Bad News

(From 2 Samuel 7:2-17; 12:1-25)

Nathan was a prophet who lived long ago when David was king of Israel. Nathan prayed and listened to God. *(Fold hands as if praying, then cup hands around ears.)* When God spoke to him, he told people what God said.

Sometimes the messages from God were good news. One time God told Nathan to give a good message to King David. How would you like to give a good message to a king? Nathan was glad to tell King David that God would make him famous and that people all over the earth would know that David was a great king.

David was a great king because he loved and trusted

God. God promised to keep David and his people safe from their enemies. And God promised that the kings of God's people would always come from David's family.

David was glad to hear Nathan's message. He promised to keep following God, and he thanked God for taking such good care of his family. How does God take care of your family?

Sometimes the messages God gave Nathan were bad news. When have you heard bad news? God sent bad news when people disobeyed and did wrong and hurtful things.

One time God sent Nathan to King David with bad news. How do you think Nathan felt about giving the king bad news?

King David had broken God's rules. One of the soldiers in King David's army had a beautiful wife named Bathsheba. David sent that soldier to the front of the battle so he would get killed. Then King David and Bathsheba got married. David did the wrong thing and God was very sad. So God sent Nathan to tell King David a story.

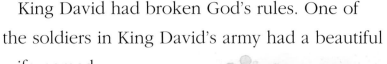

Nathan said, "Two men lived in a town. One man was rich and had lots of sheep. The other man was poor and had just one little lamb. The poor man loved the little lamb very much. He even let the little lamb eat at his table. The lamb was like a daughter to him.

"One day a traveler came to stay with the rich man. So the rich man told his servants to fix the traveler something to eat. But he didn't take a sheep from his own flocks for dinner. Instead, he took the one little lamb that belonged to the poor man."

"That's terrible!" King David said when Nathan finished his story. "He should pay the poor man back four times what he took. It was mean to take the poor man's only lamb."

Then Nathan said, "King David, you are as bad as the rich man in the story. God has blessed you with a kingdom and many wonderful things," Nathan said. "But you wanted something that didn't belong to you. You sent a soldier to die in battle so you could marry his wife."

King David hung his head and said, "I have sinned against the Lord."

"God has a message for you," Nathan said. "Because of your sin, your little baby won't be the next king."

When Nathan told David this bad news, David cried and prayed for a whole week. But the baby died. David felt sorry about the wrong things he'd done. Show how you look when you feel sorry. David prayed and asked God to forgive him.

God listened to David's prayer and forgave him. Then David felt better. A little while later, David and Bathsheba had another baby. Nathan came to see the baby and brought good news! God told Nathan to say that this baby would be the next king. Everyone clapped and celebrated when they heard the good news that Nathan brought to King David.

God still gives us good messages. We can read about them in the Bible. And if we do wrong things, we can tell God we're sorry. Then God will forgive us, just as he forgave King David.

The Wisest Man Ever

(From 1 Kings 3)

King David lived to be an old man, and he loved God all his life. Do you love God? How do you show God that you love him?

King David's son Solomon became the next king of Israel. Solomon loved God too. More than anything else, Solomon wanted to please God.

One night God spoke to King Solomon in a special dream and said, "Ask for whatever you want me to give to you."

Hmm. If you could have anything in the whole wide world, what would you ask for?

Well, Solomon could have asked for shiploads of money, but he didn't. He could have asked

for a hundred palaces, but he didn't. He could have asked for mountains of jewels, but he didn't. He could have asked to live a long, healthy life, but he didn't!

Do you know what Solomon did ask God for? He asked God to make him wise. "You have made me king over your people," Solomon prayed, "and that's a big job! I want to do it right. I want to be a good king, so please make me wise so I'll know what's right and what's wrong."

God was pleased with Solomon's choice. God said, "You didn't ask me for riches or to be famous or to live a long life. Instead you asked for wisdom to be a good king. So I will make you the wisest man in the whole world."

And that's just what happened. People from far and wide came to King Solomon for help with their problems. And with God's help, Solomon gave them the right answers.

One day two women came and stood before King Solomon's throne. They were fighting over a little baby, each trying to grab the child away from the other.

"It's my baby!" said woman number one.

"No, it's my baby!" yelled woman number two.

The first woman said, "She's lying. The baby is mine."

"No, he's mine," the second woman cried. And they started arguing all over again.

It's a good thing Solomon had asked for wisdom. He needed God's help to solve this problem. God gave Solomon an idea. King Solomon decided to play a trick to find out who the real mother was.

"Guard, draw your sword," King Solomon ordered. Let's pretend to draw our swords and wave them through the air with a big "SWISH, SWISH!"

"I know how to settle this problem. We'll cut the child in two and give each of you half."

King Solomon wouldn't really let anyone hurt the baby. He just wanted to see what the two women would say.

"No!" shouted the first woman. "Don't hurt my son. Let her have him."

The other woman started to grab the child, but King Solomon stopped her.

"Don't hurt the baby!" ordered the king. "Give him to the first woman—she is his mother."

How did Solomon know that? He knew that the real mother would never let anyone hurt her child. The trick worked!

Everyone was amazed at Solomon's wisdom. All the people in Israel said, "Our king is the wisest man in the world because his wisdom comes from God."

Just as God gave wisdom to King Solomon, God can give you wisdom, too. Just remember to pray, and God will help you grow wiser every day.

Elisha's Miracle Cure

(From 2 Kings 5:1-27)

Naaman was a mighty soldier
Who was used to winning wars.
(Make a muscle.)
But the soldier had a problem
(shake head sadly)—
His skin was full of sores.
(Rub arms.)

Naaman's sickness wouldn't leave him—
It grew bigger day by day.
(Spread arms wider and wider.)
And there wasn't any ointment
That could make the sores go 'way.
(Rub arms.)

But there was a cure for Naaman
(hold up index finger and nod);
There was hope for Naaman's life.
A Hebrew slave girl knew the answer,
So she spoke to Naaman's wife.
(Pretend to whisper in someone's ear.)

"In my country of Samaria
(point off to distance),
There lives a holy man.
If anyone can make him well,
I'm sure Elisha can!"
(Clap hands.)

The king said, "Naaman, go today!
(Walk in place.)
Take Israel's king this letter
And take this gold and silver, too.
(Hold out hands.)
I hope you'll soon be better!"

So Naaman went to Israel's king
Who said, "This isn't right.
(Frown and shake head.)
I am not God! I cannot heal!
(Shrug shoulders.)
You're trying to pick a fight!"

When Elisha heard of Naaman,
He said, "Send the man to me!
(Point to self.)
I will cure him of his sores.
He'll learn of God, you'll see!"
(Point upward.)

So Naaman, with his chariots,
Rode to Elisha's gate.
(Pretend to drive chariot.)
But the prophet didn't step outside.
So Naaman had to wait.
(Shrug.)

Then Elisha sent instructions
For Naaman to obey:
"Dip in the river seven times
(flash seven fingers)
And watch your sores go away!"
(Spread arms out wide.)

Just washing seemed too easy,
And Naaman was very proud.

(Cross arms over chest and frown.)
He said, "Let that prophet wave his hands
And call God's name out loud!
(Wave both hands in air.)

"Aren't our rivers just as good
(ripple fingers from left to right)
As the one he sends me to?"
Then angry Naaman cried out
(put hands on hips and frown),
"This washing I won't do!"
(Shake finger in air.)

"Oh, Master," Naaman's servants begged,
"Just do it—won't you try?
(Hold hands out, imploring.)
If he'd told you something hard to do,
You'd do it without asking why!"

So Naaman went to the river
And waded right on in.
(Ripple fingers left to right.)
And when he dipped down seven times

56

(stand and sit seven times),
The sores disappeared from his skin!
(Throw hands in air joyfully).

Naaman returned to Elisha's house
(Walk fingers across palm.)
To thank him and to say,
"Your God will be my God now
(point upward, then put hand over heart),
And it's only to him I'll pray!"
(Fold hands.)

Elisha helped Naaman learn of God.
(Point upward.)
Naaman's slave girl helped him too.
Telling others about the Lord
Is a job for us all to do!
(Point to self.)

A Fine, Young King

(From 2 Kings 22:1–23:25)

Josiah became king at the age of 8. Let's see...how many is eight? Eight is this many. *(Show eight fingers.)* How old are you? Josiah loved God and liked being king.

Some of the kings before Josiah didn't love God. They worshiped fake gods—idols made of wood and stone. While those bad kings ruled, they didn't take care of God's temple. But King Josiah wanted

God's temple to be clean and beautiful, so he put lots of people to work fixing it up.

The carpenters hammered *(pretend to hammer)*, the stone masons moved big blocks of stone *(pretend to move a heavy block)*, and the cleaners swept and scrubbed *(pretend to sweep, then scrub)*. And day by day, God's temple grew beautiful once again.

One day, while everyone was pounding, hammering, sweeping,

and scrubbing, the high priest found a big scroll that had been hidden by all the mess. Let's blow the dust off the scroll. One, two, three, BLOW! It turned out to be a beautiful book—the book of God's law, which had been missing for years and years. The high priest took the book of God's law to the king's secretary, who read it to King Josiah.

It told all about how God wanted his people to live. Josiah was so happy that God's book had been found. *(Draw a smile on your face.)* But he was also sad because he realized that for many years people had forgotten all about God and broken God's laws. *(Draw a frown.)*

King Josiah didn't know what to do. So he sent his best helpers to see a woman named Hulduh *(HULL-duh)*. She loved God and prayed all the time. She would know what to do.

Hulduh said that God was sad because the people had forgotten him. But God was glad, too, because King Josiah loved him and wanted to teach his people to love God and obey God's laws.

Then King Josiah called a big meeting. He stood by one of the pillars of the temple and read all the words in God's book. After the king finished reading, everyone promised to love God and obey all the things that were written in God's book.

Then King Josiah told everyone to get rid of all the fake gods and idols they had been praying to. Who are we supposed to pray to? That's right—God wants us to pray only to him. Josiah and his helpers went up into the highest hills and mountains. *(Look up.)* He went down into the deepest, darkest valleys. *(Look down.)* All

over the land he tore down the statues. CRASH! BOOM! SMASH! Finally all the fake gods were gone. *(Dust off your hands.)*

When God's temple was all fixed up and beautiful, King Josiah told the people to get ready to celebrate the Passover feast. So they held a great feast and remembered how God took care of them. It was the most wonderful Passover feast celebrated by any king. All the people praised and thanked God. What can you thank God for?

God loved King Josiah very much because Josiah taught all his people to love and obey God. You can be like Josiah. Listening to this story makes you like Josiah because you're learning God's word. Telling God you're sorry when you do wrong things makes you like Josiah too. Praying to God makes you like Josiah because he prayed and asked God to help him do what was right. Let's pray right now.

Dear God, thanks for giving us the Bible so that we can read your words. Thanks for letting us talk to you any time. We want to make you happy just as King Josiah did. Help us love you and obey you. Thank you for forgiving us when we do wrong things. Most of all, thank you for loving us. We love you too. In Jesus' name. Amen.

Nehemiah Builds a Wall

(From Nehemiah 1–2; 4; 6:1-16)

Once long ago, a man named Nehemiah *(Nee-uh-MY-uh)* served the King of Persia. Nehemiah had an important job—he stood by the king at mealtime and tasted his food and drink to make sure it wasn't poisoned. What important jobs do you have?

The king liked Nehemiah and trusted him. One day the king noticed that Nehemiah's face was very sad. Let's show our sad faces.

The king asked, "Why does your face look sad? Your heart must be sad."

Nehemiah answered, "King, may you live forever. My face is sad because the city where my family comes from is ruined and its gates are burned down."

The king asked, "What would you like to do?"

In a quick, silent prayer, Nehemiah asked God to help him. Then he said, "If you're willing, and if I've been a pleasing servant, please send me back to rebuild the city."

God answered Nehemiah's prayer! The king agreed to let Nehemiah travel to the city of

Jerusalem and rebuild it. The king even let him take wood from the royal forest and soldiers for protection. So Nehemiah set out on his journey. Let's walk our fingers up and down to show Nehemiah's long journey to Jerusalem.

Nehemiah rode around the city wall at night all by himself. The wall was crumbled and broken—anyone could walk right through. And all the gates stood charred and burned. Nehemiah wanted to start rebuilding right away, so the next day he gathered all the people and said, "Look at the walls—see how badly they're broken. Let's rebuild them and make Jerusalem beautiful again. The king himself has given us permission to do this!"

So everyone in the city worked with Nehemiah to rebuild the wall and all the gates. Let's pound our fists on top of each other as if we're building too.

When the enemies of God's people heard what was happening, they tried to stop the work. "We'll tell the king what you're doing and he'll stop you!" they warned.

But Nehemiah explained, "You're wrong. The king has sent me and God will give us success."

Even so, the three enemies tried to think of ways to keep Nehemiah from fixing the wall. Nehemiah knew they might attack at any time, so he had some people stand guard with bows and arrows while other people worked on the wall. Let's pretend to set one heavy stone on top of another one. Whew! Now let's dust off our hands.

Some people cut wood and others fastened it together to make big, heavy gates. Let's pretend to saw big pieces of wood. Families and friends worked together from the time the sun came up until the stars came out. Have you ever worked all day long? What does it feel like to work that hard?

Finally the wall stood strong and beautiful again. How does it feel to finish a tough job? Because the people finished the job so quickly, the mean enemies knew that God had helped build the wall.

Then Nehemiah and all the people of Jerusalem celebrated. They played musical instruments. What's your favorite instrument? Let's pretend to play it. As the instruments played, the people sang songs of thanksgiving and joy. The people were happy that God had helped them rebuild the wall of their city. Let's draw smiles on our faces. Now the city of God was safe, and the sound of happiness in Jerusalem could be heard from far away. Hooray—let's clap!

Contributors

Lois Keffer
Is a prolific author and editor who just can't stop writing for children and plans never to grow up.

Mike Nappa
Is a treasured teacher and editor who enjoys trying out new ideas on his adorable son, Tony.

Cindy Nelson
Is a creative writer who loves to find the fun in teaching children about God.

Joani Schultz
Is always exploding with creativity, enthusiasm, and dedication for teaching God's Word to kids of all ages.

Liz Shockey
Is a freelance writer who loves to share her gifts and her love for God's Word with children.

Jennifer Root Wilger
Is a talented editor who enjoys sharing these stories with her very own little child.

Beth Rowland Wolf
Is a gifted writer and musician who enjoys sharing her music and her faith with children.